SA's Instrument Technology Training Program is general in
nature. When maintaining any instruments in your plant,
be sure to follow the specific maintenance and safety procedures
provided by your facility and the equipment manufacturer.

D1403683

Produced by Industrial Training Corporation
for Instrument Society of America

INSTRUMENT TECHNOLOGY TRAINING PROGRAM
Instrument Calibration

ISBN 1-55617-364-4

ISA
67 Alexander Drive
P.O. Box 12277
Research Triangle Park, NC 27709
NC 919-549-8411

Student Workbook

Contents

Instrument Calibration

Using Your Training Program

This is a comprehensive videotape/text training program. It may be used for independent self-study, or in a traditional classroom setting.

The videotapes are divided into segments, varying in length from four to six minutes.

This workbook is also divided into segments that generally correspond to the videotape segments.

Throughout the workbook, you will find symbols that will help you to identify how the information is organized:

Objective
Goal

Application
Doing
Hands-On

Self-Check
Review Questions
Pre/Post Test

Bibliography
Reference/Standard

Using Your Training Program

**Calculator
Exercises
Computation**

**Concept/Idea
Understanding
Theory**

**Closer Look
More Information**

You may alternately view a segment of videotape and read the corresponding segment in your workbook. A variety of questions and practical exercises are provided to further your understanding of the subject.

If you are undertaking your training in a classroom setting, your instructor will administer a pretest and a post test during the course. Final evaluation of your progress through the training program will be based on a combination of test scores and observation of your performance during hands-on exercises.

Student Workbook

Overview

The *Instrument Calibration* training program defines the purpose of calibration and discusses the types and values of associated input and output signals. The preparations required to set up a calibration and complete a five-point check are also covered. Calibration of pneumatic and electronic instruments is demonstrated, and methods for documenting the results of calibration is demonstrated. At the end of your study, you should be able to demonstrate the training objectives for this program.

Prerequisites

The prerequisites for the *Instrument Calibration* training program include: Pneumatic Test Equipment, Electronic Test Equipment, and Primary Calibration Standards. An understanding of basic physics and math will also be helpful.

Program Objectives

Introduction

1. Explain the importance of instrument calibration.
2. Identify conditions that may require an instrument to be calibrated.
3. Select the test equipment required to calibrate pneumatic instruments.
4. Describe a calibration setup for a pneumatic instrument.
5. List several information sources to be checked before testing an instrument.
6. Explain calibration test equipment accuracy requirements.

Calibration Preparation

7. Explain the steps required to prepare an instrument for calibration, checking its calibration, and making calibration adjustments.
8. Explain the input and output connections required to calibrate a pneumatic instrument.
9. Explain the importance of the upper and lower range test point selections.
10. Given an instrument's input range, determine the input values for a five-point calibration.
11. Given an instrument's output range, calculate the ideal output for each test point.

Pneumatic Instrument Calibration

12. Describe a five-point calibration check on a pneumatic instrument, including what data to record.
13. Analyze calibration data for instrument errors.
14. Explain the adjustments made to correct zero shift, span errors, and combination errors.
15. Verify that adjustments have brought the pneumatic instrument into calibration.
16. Explain the advantages of a five-point check over a three-point check.

Calibrating an Electronic Instrument

17. Select the test equipment required to calibrate electronic instruments.
18. Describe a calibration setup for an electronic instrument.
19. Explain the input and output connections required to calibrate an electronic instrument.

20. Given an instrument's input range, determine the input values for a five-point calibration.
21. Given an instrument's output range, calculate the ideal output for each test point.
22. Describe a five-point calibration check on an electronic instrument, including what data to record.
23. Analyze calibration data for instrument errors.
24. Explain the adjustments made to correct zero shift, span errors, and combination errors.
25. Verify that adjustments have brought the electronic instrument into calibration.

Segment 1

Explain the importance of instrument calibration.

The proper operation of any process depends on the performance of each of the instruments in the loop. Instruments are calibrated to ensure that their output accurately represents the input. For example, transmitters produce an output signal that represents the value of the measured variable. The signal range for pneumatic transmitters is usually 3 to 15 psi. 3 psi represents the lowest output value, and 15 psi represents the highest output value. The signal range for electronic transmitters is usually 4 to 20 mA. Within this range, 4 mA represents the lowest output value, and 20 mA represents the highest output value. As with transmitters, all of the instruments in a loop must be calibrated so that input values to an instrument are accurately represented by the output.

Calibration is the application of measured variable values and the recording of the corresponding output or indicated values. The technique of applying an input and measuring an output is done over the entire range of the instrument, in both the upscale and downscale directions. The recorded output values or indication values are compared to desired output values to determine if any errors exist. If errors exist, the instrument must be calibrated.

When an instrument is properly calibrated, its output accurately represents its input. The instrument's range and span must be known in order to check its calibration. Range defines the highest and lowest values of the measured variable that an instrument is adjusted to measure, receive, or transmit. For example, an instrument's range may be 50 to 250 psig. Span is the algebraic difference between the upper and lower range values. So, with a range of 50 to 250 psig, the span of the instrument is 200 psig.

A pressure transmitter may have an input range of 0 to 50 psi. Its output range may be 4 to 20 mA. When the input to the transmitter is 5 psi, the output is 5.6 mA. 5 psi is 10 percent of the transmitter's input span, and 5.6 mA is 10 percent of the transmitter's output span When the input is 50 percent, the output is 12 mA, which is 50 percent of the output.

Identify conditions that may require an instrument to be calibrated.

Calibration may be checked on a routine basis to ensure that each instrument in a given loop is functioning properly. Calibration stickers are usually attached to each instrument to provide a record of the last calibration. Regularly scheduled calibration maintains the accuracy of process instrumentation. Instruments must also be calibrated before and after repair and before being returned to service after extended shutdowns. Instruments may also require calibration if:

- The product fails to meet specifications
- A new instrument is installed in a loop
- The installed position of the instrument must be changed

Instrument calibration should be verified before installing new instruments. Although instruments are usually factory calibrated, the calibration can be affected by rough handling in shipping or transit. Calibration is a diagnostic tool that will indicate instrument problems prior to their being repaired. After repair, instruments must be recalibrated to verify their accuracy. Also, changes in the mounting positions of instruments can affect the relationship of the internal components, so instruments should be calibrated in the positions in which they are, or will be, installed in the process. After extended shutdowns, instrument calibration should be checked because process materials and environmental conditions can adversely affect calibration over time.

Select the test equipment required to calibrate pneumatic instruments.

Before calibrating an instrument, its operation, as well as the types and values of the input and output signals, must be known and understood. A calibration set-up must simulate the process values to be measured by the instrument under test. The preparations required for all calibrations must include the elements needed to supply precise inputs and accurately measure the outputs.

Describe a calibration setup for a pneumatic instrument.

In the example shown in the videotape, the instrument under test was a pneumatic pressure transmitter, which senses process pressure in the range of 0 to 25 pounds, and produces a pneumatic output signal, which varies between 3 and 15 pounds. In this application a variable pressure source is required to simulate the process pressure. Air pressure can be used if the instrument has a relatively low range. A dead weight tester can be used to test higher range instruments. To ensure accurate values of input pressure, a secondary standard, such as a test gage, is also connected to the input pressure source. The input pressure source and the input standard may be two separate devices. However, both of these functions may be contained in a single calibration device for low pressure calibration, for pressures below 30 psi.

All instruments require a power supply. The exact power supply requirements for an instrument are specified by the manufacturer. The type of output standard used depends on the type of output signal. In this example, the pneumatic transmitter's power supply is 20 pound instrument air. A test gage is connected to the transmitter to accurately monitor the values of its output signals.

List several information sources to be checked before testing an instrument.

Manufacturer's instructions and facility guidelines should be reviewed before testing and calibrating an instrument. These sources usually provide information that will help to achieve accurate test results. For example, the manufacturer's instructions usually provide:

- accuracy ratings and the test conditions for determining the ratings
- adjustment points for zero, span, and linearity
- diagrams that show the recommended setup for the calibration equipment
- information that details the required accuracy rating for the input and output standards

Explain calibration test equipment accuracy requirements.

Ideally, the secondary standard should be at least ten times more accurate than the instrument being tested. For example, if the instrument's accuracy rating is plus or minus 1 percent of span, the secondary standard's rating should be plus or minus 0.1 percent of span or better.

Hands-On Exercises

1. Locate the instrument loop diagram for a simple control loop in your facility.

2. Identify the components in the loop and review the manufacturer's instructions for calibrating each component.

Review Questions

1. What is the purpose of instrument calibration?

2. True or False. When an instrument is properly calibrated, the output span matches the input span.

3. Which of the following situations may require that an instrument be calibrated?
   a. Transferring the instrument to a new control loop
   b. Following the repair of the instrument
   c. Installation of a new instrument
   d. All of the above

4. Information on the recommended setup for a calibration can usually be found in
   a. Instrument loop diagrams
   b. Instructions on the use of primary standards
   c. Manufacturer's instructions
   d. None of the above

Segment 2

Explain the steps required to prepare an instrument for calibration, checking its calibration, and making adjustments.

Calibration equipment connections must not introduce errors into the test results. To eliminate this possibility, always make sure that pneumatic instrument connections are tight and do not leak. For example, loose connections that permit leakage could result in erroneous indications. The connection points for calibration of either electronic or pneumatic instruments are similar in that both types of instruments require an input signal source, a power supply, and a method of monitoring output values.

Explain the input and output connections required to calibrate a pneumatic instrument.

To make the connections necessary to calibrate a pneumatic pressure transmitter, follow these steps:

1. *Set the supply air pressure to the minimum pressure.*

2. *Make the connections necessary to supply and measure the input signal by connecting tubing to the regulator outlets and the transmitter.*
   The regulator supplies the pressure signal that simulates the process pressure. Tubing is first connected to the regulator outlet and then to the test gage.

3. *Connect the transmitter's output to the test gage.*
   Ideally, the output standard should be at least ten times more accurate than the instrument being calibrated. In the example shown in the videotape, the test gage has an accuracy rating of .02 percent. Since the transmitter's accuracy rating is plus or minus .33 percent, the output standard is at least ten times more accurate than the transmitter.

4. *Connect the specified supply air to the transmitter.*
   This supply provides the air pressure necessary to produce the output signal. Since the maximum output signal pressure is fifteen pounds, a 20 pound supply provides sufficient pressure to operate the transmitter.

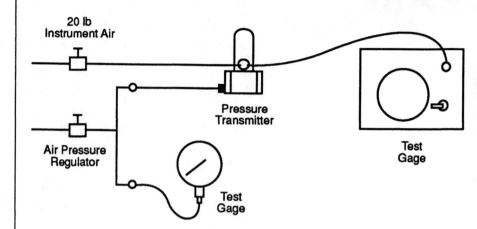

This figure represents the instrument connections needed to set up the calibration for the pneumatic transmitter used as an example in the videotape.

To check the calibration of a pneumatic transmitter, follow these steps:

1. *Supply the instrument being tested with instrument air.*

2. *Adjust the calibration air pressure regulator until the desired pressure is indicated on the test gage.*

3. *Apply the input signal to the transmitter.*

4. *Read the value of the transmitter's output signal on the test gage.*

5. *Supply other input values to the transmitter by adjusting the calibration air pressure.*

Explain the importance of the upper and lower range test point selections.

Determining the input test points is an important part of every calibration procedure. Although there are no firm rules on the values of input span that should be used for calibration test points, general guidelines are available.

1. *Distribute the test points over the instrument's entire range.*

2. *Include values at 10 percent of the lower and upper range values.*

3. *Use a minimum of five test points to detect all of the possible types of nonlinearity errors.*

4. *Do not include 0 or 100 percent of span in the five test points selected for the calibration.* **Note:** *Readings taken at 0 percent may result in inconsistent values because it is not possible to approach 0 from the low side. Readings taken at 100 percent may overrange the instrument, especially if it is approached from the high side.*

In many applications, 0 percent output is not represented by a total lack of an output signal. Usually, 0 percent output is represented by a minimum value known as a "live zero." Having a live zero helps determine if an instrument's output exactly represents 0 input. For example, if process conditions caused the instrument's output to try to go below 0 percent, the output would be below the "(live) zero" level.

Given an instrument's input range, determine the input values for a five-point calibration.

A calibration cycle is a series of readings taken on both upscale and downscale traverses. Unless test points are selected properly and checked efficiently, the effects of dead band and hysteresis can adversely affect the results of the check. To ensure that the test results are valid, follow these steps:

1. *Always approach test points from the same direction to reduce the effects of dead band and hysteresis. Upscale readings are approached from the low side. Down scale readings are approached from the high side.*

2. *Unless otherwise specified, assume that 10 percent and 90 percent are valid test points for the low and high ends of an instrument's range.*

The five-point check in the videotape example, the values selected represented 10, 30, 50, 70, and 90 percent of the instrument's input range.

After the percent of input span values has been determined, it is necessary to calculate the input values that correspond to each percent of span. To calculate these values, follow these steps:

1. *Identify the span of the instrument. Multiply the span by the percent of span required and add that value to the lower range limit.*

2. *Calculate the input values that correspond to each percent of span.*
   For example, assume the range of the transmitter is 0 to 25 pounds. Therefore, the instrument's span is 25 pounds. To calculate the input pressure value that corresponds to 10 percent of span, multiply the span by 10 percent and add that value to the lower range limit. The ten percent value is 2.5 psi. 30 percent of 25 psi is 7.5 psi. When 7.5 psi is added to the lower range value of 0 psi, the test value at 30 percent equals 7.5 psi.

3. *Record each input value in the corresponding test value space on the appropriate form.*

4. *Compute the ideal output values using the same method.*
   For example, the output span is 12 psi. The expected 10 percent output value is equal to 10 percent of the output span plus the output lower range value. 10 percent of span is 1.2 psi, and the lower range value is 3 psi. The expected output value is 4.2 psi.

5. *Record each ideal output value in the corresponding test value space on the appropriate form.*
   Many facilities have standard calibration data sheets, which have spaces for recording:
   • Specific facility and instrument identification information.
   • Calibration input and output data. Space is usually available to record the results of several upscale and downscale checks.

6. *As appropriate, exercise the instrument being tested. Vary its input through several full-scale transitions to help reduce the effects of hysteresis. This should be done before you begin the calibration.*
   Any instrument that has moving mechanical parts as part of its input or output section should be exercised prior to calibration. This classification is likely to include all pneumatic instruments and many electronic instruments.

Calibration Preparation

Hands-On Exercise

1. Review the guidelines provided by your facility on calibration procedures.

2. Note any specific instructions related to the methods needed to set up or prepare for the calibration of pneumatic or electronic instruments.

Review Questions

1. Instrument connections should be checked to ensure that they are
   a. Leak-free
   b. Tight
   c. Shiny
   d. All of the above

2. Ideally, the output standard selected for calibration should be _____ times greater than the device under test.

3. The test points selected for calibration should include values _____ 10 percent of the upper and lower range values.

4. Test points should always be approached from the _____ direction.

Segment 3

Describe a five-point calibration check on a pneumatic instrument, and specify the data that should be recorded.

To calibrate an instrument, using a five-point calibration check, follow these steps:

1. *Apply the input value to the instrument.*
   Assume the following input values: 10 percent, 30 percent, 50 percent, 70 percent, and 90 percent. It is imperative to approach each value from below if the upscale check is done first. Take care not to exceed the test pressure on any of the upscale checks. If you find that you have exceeded the test point, reduce the pressure below the desired pressure and begin again.

2. *Allow the instrument to stabilize at its final output value after you have reached the desired pressure.*

3. *Record the upscale output reading in the appropriate space on the data sheet, and note the next upscale value to be applied to the instrument.*

4. *Increase the input pressure to the next upscale value, and repeat Steps 1-3 until each of the upscale test points has been checked.*

5. *Apply the downscale input values. Approach the downscale input values from above.*
   For example, to check the 90 percent downscale value, raise the input pressure above 22.5 psi and then slowly lower it back down. As with upscale checks, be sure not to overshoot the input pressures during the downscale checks.

6. *Record the output pressure value on the data sheet, and note the next upscale value to be applied to the instrument.*

7. *Increase the input pressure to the next upscale value, and repeat Steps 1-3 until each of the upscale test points has been checked.*

8. *Lower the pressure applied to the instrument to a value below the value of the first input.*

9. *Complete and record a minimum of three complete calibration cycles.*

After completing the downscale checks, continue to lower the input pressure below 2.5 psi to begin the second calibration cycle. It is advisable to complete and record several calibration cycles. Multiple cycles provide a good baseline of data on which to base the error analysis and corrective actions. After completing three calibration cycles, evaluate the output values recorded in the data sheet for any apparent instrument errors.

Analyze calibration data for instrument errors.

After obtaining the results of the three calibration cycles on the instrument, analyze the readings. In the example shown in the videotape, the readings for the pneumatic pressure transmitter revealed two instrument errors.

Explain the adjustments made to correct zero shift, span errors, and combination errors.

A zero shift error was indicated because both the upscale and downscale values recorded at 10 percent were consistently higher than the ideal values. In addition, although the upscale and downscale 90 percent values were very close to the ideal values, a span error existed. The zero shift error caused the 10 percent readings to be higher than ideal. If there were no span error, the 90 percent readings would also have been higher than the ideal values. Since the actual 90 percent readings were not higher than the ideal values, it can be concluded that the instrument's span is too small. The consistency of the upscale and downscale readings for each of the three cycles indicates the absence of hysteresis error. Hysteresis error is usually largest at the 50 percent test point.

Although closely scrutinizing the data can help to determine instrument errors, it is usually best to plot the calibration curves. Plotting the curves gives a visual picture of the errors.

The input/output curve (see facing page) for the first calibration cycle reveals, by the shape and position of the calibration curve, the zero shift and span error. The manufacturer's instructions frequently explain the calibration adjustments needed to correct such errors. Zero is usually adjusted first.

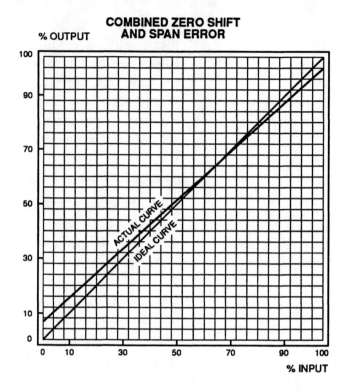

COMBINED ZERO SHIFT AND SPAN ERROR

To correct zero shift on a pneumatic transmitter, apply the 10 percent input pressure to the transmitter. Adjust the output to the proper value for a 10 percent input by turning the zero adjustment screw. This adjustment provides an accurate starting point for the span adjustment. Next, increase the input pressure to the 90 percent value and adjust the span.

Verify that adjustments have brought the pneumatic instrument into calibration.

Adjustments for zero shift and span error affect each other, so it is necessary to recheck the 10 percent value. If necessary, readjust the zero setting. Continue this technique until no further adjustments are needed for zero or span.

Complete another calibration cycle to verify that the adjustments eliminated the zero shift and span errors. Make additional adjustments if the instrument does not meet specifications. Record the calibration results in accordance with your facility procedures. This instrument did not have a linearity error; however, calibration data and curves should always be checked for linearity problems.

Explain the advantages of a five-point check over a three-point check.

Linearity errors frequently show up in the form of an 'S'-shaped calibration curve. In the example shown in the videotape, a three-point calibration check of the 0, 50, and 100 percent inputs would not have indicated the problem. This type of error demonstrates the need for using at least five points in a calibration check. Pneumatic instruments usually require mechanical adjustments to correct linearity problems. Consult the manufacturer's literature for specific information concerning linearity adjustments.

Hands-On Exercises

1. Identify the equipment required to produce and measure the necessary input standards to calibrate a pneumatic instrument that you may be working with in the future. Determine the input values necessary to perform a five-point calibration check.

2. Review the manufacturer's literature to determine how to correct specific instrument errors, such as zero shift and span.

Review Questions

1. It is unlikely that _____ errors will be discerned in a three-point calibration check.

2. When upscale checks are performed first, values should be approached from above/below.

3. It is important to allow the output value to _____ before recording the data.

4. If zero shift and span errors are revealed in the data from the test, zero shift/span should be corrected first.

Segment 4

Select test equipment required to calibrate electronic instruments.

The equipment for calibrating electronic instruments is similar in function to that required for pneumatic instrument calibration. In the example shown in the videotape, a three-wire RTD temperature transmitter with an input range of 0 to 100 degrees C and an output range of 4 to 20 mA is calibrated using a five-point calibration check.

A temperature calibrator serves as both the input signal source and the input standard. The calibrator in the demonstration is similar to a decade box.

The power for the instrument is supplied by a regulated DC power supply. The power supply for electronic instrument calibrations must be set to supply the specific voltage required to operate the transmitter. Usually, when an instrument is installed in a process loop, the controller supplies the power to operate the instrument.

A milliammeter is connected in series with the transmitter output terminals and the power supply to accurately monitor the transmitter's output. For electronic instrument calibrations, multifunction calibrators could be used instead of separate input and output calibration devices. Most multifunction calibrators can supply and monitor the input as well as monitor the output.

Describe a calibration setup for an electronic instrument.

The setup for the calibration requires several electrical connections. In this example, the first step is to connect the three wires that connect the temperature calibrator to the transmitter. Refer to the manufacturer's literature for specific instructions on how to make the connections between the calibration test equipment and the device under test.

It is a good idea to make connections to the instrument being tested first. Then make the connections to the other calibration equipment. As with pneumatic instruments, it is imperative that the electronic instrument calibration connections not introduce any errors or extra resistance into the calibration circuit. Ensure that all connections are tight. Use lugs on wires when appropriate. Avoid making connections with alligator clips.

Calibrating an Electronic Instrument

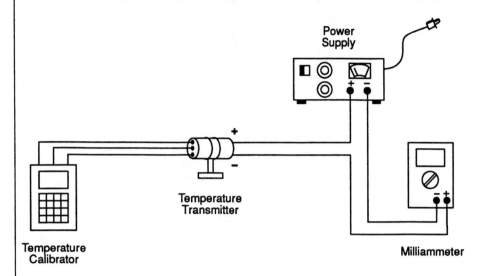

Power Supply

Temperature Transmitter

Temperature Calibrator

Milliammeter

With the input circuit connected, make up the series output circuit, which includes the transmitter's output terminals, the milliammeter, and the power supply. Start by connecting the power supply's positive output terminal to the transmitter's positive terminal. Then, connect the transmitter's negative terminal to the milliammeter's positive terminal. Complete the series output circuit by connecting the milliammeter's negative terminal to the power supply's negative terminal. This figure represents the calibration connections for this example.

Explain the input and output connections required to calibrate an electronic instrument.

The temperature calibrator simulates a three-wire RTD that provides the various input signals to the transmitter. The desired resistance values must be entered into the calibrator. The power supply, shown in this program, provides the power to operate the transmitter's electronics. The transmitter's electronics supply the output signal. The transmitter's output terminals serve a dual purpose: the terminals serve as the connection point for the transmitter's output signal and as the power supply connections. This type of transmitter is referred to as 'loop driven,' or 'two wire,' which means that it receives its power from the output loop. In this example, the output standard is a milliammeter that must be connected in series in order to measure the output current.

Given an instrument's input range, determine the input values for a five-point calibration.

After the calibration connections are made, the temperatures corresponding to the five-point check must be calculated. This transmitter is designed to operate within a range of 0 to 100 degrees, so the span is 100 degrees.

Apply the same technique used to determine the pneumatic instrument's input values to the calibration of electronic instruments. In this example, the value is 10 degrees. 10 percent of a 100 degree span is 10 degrees. Add a 0 degree minimum range value and the electronic instrument input value equals 10 degrees. Each test point must be calculated and recorded on the appropriate form. Then, the ideal output values are calculated and entered onto the data sheet. In this example, the values are based on an output range of 4 to 20 mA and a span of 16 mA.

Describe a five-point calibration check on an electronic instrument including what data to record.

To start the calibration, properly position the milliammeter and energize the power supply. Enter the first percent value into the calibrator to start the upscale check. When the instrument's output has stabilized, record the value on the data sheet. Continue to check the remaining upscale test points. Although electronic instruments are not typically susceptible to detectable hysteresis and dead band errors, it is a good idea to also do a downscale check. After the desired number of calibration cycles has been completed, plot the calibration curves on an input/output graph.

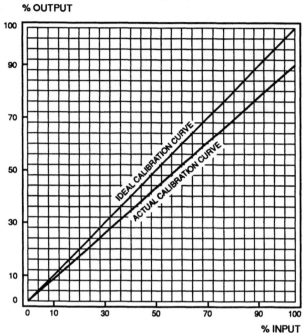

SPAN ERROR

This figure shows the resulting calibration curve for the temperature transmitter. Zero shift does not appear, so the zero point is correct. However, the curve reveals that the span does need to be adjusted.

Explain adjustments made to correct zero shift, span errors and combination errors.

In this example, 90 degrees is the value used to simulate the 90 percent test point. This value is entered in the calibrator. The span pot is adjusted to raise the output to the proper value: 18.4 mA. Since span adjustments may affect the zero point, always recheck the 10 percent test point and adjust zero as necessary. After zero and span are properly adjusted, run another calibration cycle to verify the results of the adjustments.

Hands-On Exercises

1.   Identify the equipment required to produce and measure the necessary input standards to calibrate an electronic instrument that you may be working with in the future. Determine the input values necessary to perform a five-point calibration check.

2. Review the manufacturer's literature to determine how to correct specific instrument errors, such as zero shift and span.

Review Questions

1. In process loops, electronic instruments, such as transmitters, generally receive power from the _____.

2. When making a downscale check, values should be approached from above/below.

3. When milliammeters are used as output standards, they must always be connected in series/parallel with the instrument under test.

4. After any required adjustments have been made, another _____ should verify the results of the adjustments.

Review Questions — Introduction

1. What is the purpose of instrument calibration?
   Instruments are calibrated to ensure that their output accurately represents the input.

2. True. When an instrument is properly calibrated, the output span matches the input span.

3. Which of the following situations may require that an instrument be calibrated?
   d. All of the above

4. Information on the recommended setup for a calibration can usually be found in
   c. Manufacturer's instructions

Review Questions — Calibration Preparation

1. Instrument connections should be checked to ensure that they are
   a. Leak-free
   b. Tight

2. Ideally, the output standard selected for calibration should be 10 times greater than the device under test.

3. The test points selected for calibration should include values at or within 10 percent of the upper and lower range values.

4. Test points should always be approached from the same direction.

Review Questions — Pneumatic Instrumet Calibration

1. It is unlikely that linearity errors will be discerned in a three-point calibration check.

2. When upscale checks are performed first, values should be approached from below.

3. It is important to allow the output value to stabilize before recording the data.

4. If zero shift and span errors are revealed in the data from the test, zero shift should be corrected first.

Review Questions — Calibrating an Electronic Instrument

1. In process loops, electronic instruments, such as transmitters, generally receive power from the controller.

2. When making a downscale check, values should be approached from above

3. When milliammeters are used as output standards, they must always be connected in series with the instrument under test.

4. After any required adjustments have been made, another calibration cycle should verify the results of the adjustments.

Glossary

Accuracy

In process instrumentation, degree of conformity of an indicated value to a recognized accepted standard value or ideal value.

Calibration

Determination of the experimental relationship between the quantity being measured and the output of the device that measures it, where the quantity measured is obtained through a recognized standard of measurement.

Hysteresis

1. A phenomenon demonstrated by materials that make their behavior a function of the history of the environment to which they have been subjected. Hysteresis is usually determined by subtracting the value of dead band from the maximum measured separation between upscale-going and downscale-going indications of the measured variable (during a full range traverse, unless otherwise specified) after transients have decayed. This measurement is sometimes called hysteresis error or hysteretic error. Some reversal of output may be expected for any reversal of input; this distinguishes hysteresis from dead band. 2. The tendency of an instrument to give a different output for a given input, depending on whether the input resulted from an increase or decrease from the previous value.

Linearity

The closeness to which the curve relating two variables approximates a straight line. It is usually expressed as the maximum deviation between the actual curve and the best -fit straight line.

Primary instrument

An instrument that can be calibrated without reference to another instrument.

Range

1. For instrumentation, the set of values over which measurements can be made without changing the instrument's sensitivity. 2. The extent of a measuring, indicating, or recording scale. 3. The set of values that a quantity or function may assume. 4. The difference between the highest and lowest value that a quantity or function may assume.

Span

1. The algebraic difference between the upper and lower range values; thus, a temperature in the range of 20 °C to 250° has a span of 230 °C. 2. The difference between maximum and minimum calibrated measurement values. Example: an instrument having a calibrated range of 20-120 has a span of 100.

Standard gage

A highly accurate gage used only as a reference standard for checking or calibrating working gages.

Test gage A pressure gage specially built for test service or other types of work that require a high degree of accuracy and repeatability.

Zero Shift A shift in the instrument calibrated span evidenced by a change in the zero value. Usually caused by temperature changes, overrange, or vibration of the instrument.

Bibliography

ISA Publications

Application Concepts of Process Control. P. W. Murrill. Instrument Society of America, Research Triangle Park, NC. 1988.
(ISBN: 1-55617-171-4)

Automatic Tuning of PID Controllers. K. J. Astrom and T. Hagglund. Instrument Society of America, Research Triangle Park, NC. 1988.
(ISBN: 1-55617-081-5)

Electronic Controllers. L. M. Thompson. Instrument Society of America, Research Triangle Park, NC. 1989.
(ISBN: 1-555617-129-3)

Flow Measurement. D. W. Spitzer, ed. Instrument Society of America, Research Triangle Park, NC. 1991.
(ISBN: 1-555617-334-2)

Fundamentals of Flow Measurement. J. P. DeCarlo. Instrument Society of America, Research Triangle Park, NC. 1984.
(ISBN: 0-087664-627-5)

Fundamentals of Process Control Theory., 2nd ed. P. W. Murrill. Instrument Society of America, Research Triangle Park, NC. 1981.
(ISBN: 0-87664-507-4)

Industrial Flow Measurement, 2nd ed. D. W. Spitzer. Instrument Society of America, Research Triangle Park, NC. 1990.
(ISBN: 1-555617-243-5)

Industrial Pressure Measurement. D. R. Gillum. Instrument Society of America, Research Triangle Park, NC. 1982.
(ISBN: 0-87664-668-2)

Measurement and Control of Liquid Level. C. H. Cho. Instrument Society of America, Research Triangle Park, NC. 1982.
(ISBN: 0-87664-625-9)

Process Control Fundamentals Package. Instrument Society of America, Research Triangle Park, NC. 1987.
(ISBN: 1-55617-195-1)

Temperature Measurement in Industry. E. C. Magison. Instrument Society of America, Research Triangle Park, NC. 1990.
(ISBN: 1-55617-208-7)

Bibliography

Standards and Recommended Practices

The Comprehensive Dictionary of Instrumentation and Control.
Instrument Society of America, Research Triangle Park, NC.
(ISBN: 1-55617-125-0)

ANSI/ISA-S5.1, *Instrumentation Symbols and Identification.*
Instrument Society of America, Research Triangle Park, NC. 1984.
(ISBN: 0-87664-844-8)

ANSI/ISA-S5.4, *Instrument Loop Diagrams.* Instrument Society of
America, Research Triangle Park, NC. 1976 (Revised 1989).
(ISBN: 1-55617-227-3)

ANSI/ISA-S5.5, *Graphic Symbols for Process Displays.* Instrument
Society of America, Research Triangle Park, NC. 1985 (Approved
1986). (ISBN: 0-87664-935-5)

ANSI/ISA-S51.1, *Process Instrumentation Terminology.* Instrument
Society of America, Research Triangle Park, NC. 1979.
(ISBN: 0-87664-390-4)

Videotapes

Instrumentation Video Series. Instrument Society of America,
Research Triangle Park, NC. 1985, 1986, 1987, 1988.

Continuous Process Control Series. Instrument Society of America,
Research Triangle Park, NC. 1989.

Control Technology and Application Series. Instrument Society of
America, Research Triangle Park, NC. 1988.

Industrial Measurement Series. Instrument Society of America,
Research Triangle Park, NC. 1987.

INVOLVE® Interactive Videodisc Instruction

Controller Tuning Series
Instrument Society of America, Research Triangle Park, NC. 1990.

Electronic Maintenance Series
Instrument Society of America, Research Triangle Park, NC. 1991.

Industrial Process Control Series
Instrument Society of America, Research Triangle Park, NC. 1991.

Interpreting Process Control Diagrams
Instrument Society of America, Research Triangle Park, NC. 1990.

Troubleshooting Series
Instrument Society of America, Research Triangle Park, NC. 1990.

Index